D0264917

GULLIVER'S TRAVELS

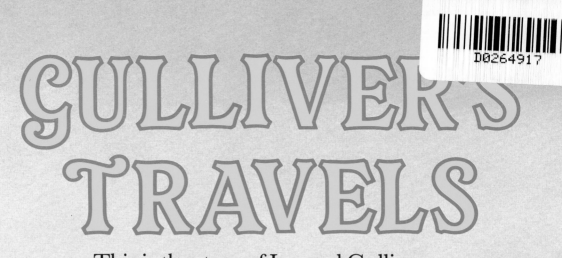

This is the story of Lemuel Gulliver, a man who lived about two hundred and fifty years ago. He studied very hard and after many years, he became a doctor. He longed to travel and loved the sea, so he became a doctor on board a sailing ship.

One day he set off on a long voyage to the South Seas on a ship called the Antelope — and here begins one of the strangest adventure stories ever told.

All went well on the Antelope for the first few weeks. Then suddenly one night, a great storm sprang up, the ship hit a rock and was wrecked.

Although the sea was rough and the waves high, Gulliver was such a strong swimmer that he managed to reach the shore. Completely exhausted, he dragged himself up the beach as far away from the sea as possible. He lay down on the first grassy bank he found and fell into a deep sleep.

At daybreak, when he opened his eyes, he tried to sit up and look around — but he was tied to the ground! He couldn't move his arms or legs or even lift his head.

Then Gulliver felt something alive running up his legs and across his chest — like a crowd of mice or several beetles perhaps!

All at once, Gulliver let out a great roar of surprise. For standing on his chest were at least forty men, each about six inches high. Gulliver's great roar startled the little men. Quickly they slid down to the floor below, where great crowds of tiny people were assembled.

As Gulliver tried to turn his head to look, the strings that bound his arms snapped. This frightened the little people so much, that they shot hundreds of their sharp arrows into his face.

Although this hurt quite a bit, Gulliver decided to lie still and not to frighten the little people again. After a while, when they had walked all over Gulliver, they became quite brave and tried to talk to him. But the little folk spoke a different language, so Gulliver couldn't understand a single word.

Somehow their tiny Emperor realised that the giant man they had captured, by now must be very hungry. So he gave orders that a tall wooden platform be built, to reach Gulliver's mouth.

After a while, several cartloads of food and wine arrived. And hundreds of the tiny men climbed up the platform with baskets of bread and meat. The hungry Gulliver drank a whole barrel of their wine in one gulp, and a basket full of loaves in one bite.

The Lilliputians (for that is what the little people were called) kept bringing more and more until Gulliver was so full up, he fell fast asleep.

The little people seemed to have lost all fear of the gigantic Gulliver, so while he slept, thousands of them set to work. Five hundred carpenters made a platform on wheels, and nine hundred men hoisted the sleeping Gulliver onto it. Then with five hundred guards either side and one thousand five hundred horses pulling hard, they began to move him towards their capital city.

It took a whole day and night to reach their destination. At last the procession came to a halt outside a large church, which was to be Gulliver's house — although it seemed as small as a dog kennel to him.

The tiny Emperor of Lilliput did not intend setting Gulliver free altogether. He ordered all his blacksmiths to make a thick chain and padlock it onto Gulliver's leg, so he could move around — but not very far.

News soon spread of the giant the Emperor had captured. People flocked in from all over the land of Lilliput, until the city was jammed with the little folk.

Six hundred of them were chosen to look after Gulliver, and four hundred tailors were kept busy making him new clothes. Six of Lilliput's finest scholars were sent to teach him their language.

At last the Emperor could understand Gulliver when he asked to be set free. He finally agreed, on one condition. Gulliver must empty his pockets of anything that could be dangerous to Lilliput.

Out came a knife, a comb and a razor. The little people were fascinated. Then came his handkerchief — which to them looked like a carpet. His snuffbox seemed like a huge chest full of gunpowder; his watch made more noise than a watermill, and they thought that his purse was a fishing net.

Finally Gulliver took out his pistol and fired it into the air. So great was the noise, thousands of the little people fell flat on their backs with shock. Only the Emperor stood his ground. For a man only six inches high, he was very brave.

But even the brave Emperor feared
something. And one day he came to ask Gulliver's help.

On the island of nearby Blefuscu lived a people
called the Big-Endians. Their fleet of fifty ships had
just set sail to invade Lilliput.

What a shock the poor Big-Endian sailors got
when Gulliver waded out to sea, roped all their ships
together, and dragged them back to Lilliput.

It didn't take Gulliver very long to realise that
the Emperor of Lilliput was only using him to fight his
battles for him, and that the Big-Endians were not a
wicked people at all. So Gulliver made his mind up to
go over to their island and live with them.

He took a large warship from Lilliput, loaded it up with his clothes (so they wouldn't get wet), then towed it behind him to their island of Blefuscu.

He was most kindly received by the little folk, but all Gulliver really wanted was to get back to England.

Quite by chance as Gulliver was walking on top of the cliff, he saw something floating in the sea. He could hardly believe his eyes — it was a full size rowing boat floating upside down.

Straight away the Emperor of the Big-Endians sent every ship in his fleet out to sea to tow it back to shore.

It took two thousand men to turn the boat right side up and then begin to repair it. Five hundred people stitched day and night to make the sails. Everyone on the island worked hard until the boat was ready.

Gulliver took on board several tiny live sheep and cows to take back home. Then sadly came the time to say farewell.

After only two days at sea, Gulliver was picked up by a sailing ship heading for England. When he told his strange story, the captain could hardly believe it — until he saw the tiny cows and sheep which Gulliver placed on the table in front of him.

At last Gulliver returned home. People were delighted to welcome him back, and never tired of hearing his strange story.

THE FROG PRINCE

Once upon a time there lived a King who had several beautiful daughters, but the youngest was even more beautiful than the rest.

Near the castle of this King was a large and gloomy forest. Just a short walk into the trees was a small clearing. At the far side stood an old lime tree, and beneath its branches splashed a fountain in the middle of a dark deep pool.

Whenever it was very hot, the King's youngest daughter would run off into this wood and sit by the pool, throwing her golden ball into the air. This was her very favourite pastime.

One afternoon when the Princess threw the ball high up in the air — she didn't catch it! It slipped through her fingers onto the grass. Then it rolled past her into the fountain, and disappeared beneath the water.

The Princess peered into the pool, but her precious golden ball was gone. Quickly, she plunged her arms into the pool as far as she could reach, but she could feel nothing except weeds and water lilies. Some people said the pool was so deep — it had no bottom. So when the Princess realised her golden ball was gone for ever, she began to cry. ''Come back to me this minute, golden ball,'' sobbed the Princess, staring hard into the water.

Now as a rule, Princesses are used to getting their own way. So after her golden ball didn't magically pop up out of the water, she started to howl even louder. Dear, oh dear! First she stamped her feet and then she threw herself down on the grass in temper.

The Princess was making so much noise, that she didn't notice a big green frog stick his head out of the water and jump onto the grass beside her. ''Don't cry, beautiful Princess,'' the frog croaked. ''I saw your golden ball fall into the water, and it will be my pleasure to dive down and get it for you — if you will give me something in return.''

At this the Princess cheered up. "I will gladly give you my jewels and pearls, even my golden crown. If you will bring back my golden ball." It's true to say that promises should never be made in a hurry, even by Princesses, because a promise is a thing that must be kept — especially to frogs!

The frog hopped nearer to the Princess. "Pearls and jewels and golden crowns are no use to me," he went on, "but if you'll love me and be my friend, if you'll let me eat from your golden plate, drink from your golden cup, and sleep on your golden bed, I will dive down and fetch your ball."

So eager was the Princess to see her golden ball once more, that she didn't listen too carefully to what the frog had to say. "I promise you all you ask, if only you will bring back my ball."

Quick as a flash, the frog jumped into the pool then bobbed up again with the ball in his mouth. Straight away the King's daughter snatched her ball and ran back to the castle.

"Take me with you," cried the frog. "I cannot run as fast as you and I shall be left behind."

But the Princess didn't care about her promise and soon forgot all about the frog. Later that day, when the Princess was sitting at the table, something was heard coming up the marble stairs, ''Splish, splosh.'' The sound came nearer and nearer and a voice cried, ''Let me in, youngest daughter of the King.''

The Princess jumped up to see who had called her. Now when she caught sight of the frog, she turned very pale.

''What does a frog want with you?'' demanded the King, looking rather surprised.

The Princess hung her head. ''When I was sitting playing by the fountain my golden ball fell into the water. This frog fetched it back for me — because I cried so much.'' The Princess started to cry again. ''I promised to love him and let him eat from my golden plate, drink from my golden cup, and sleep on my golden bed.''

The King looked at the frog and thought for a while before he spoke. ''Then you must keep your promise, my daughter.''

The Princess knew she must obey, so she beckoned the frog to come inside. The frog hopped in after her and jumped up into her chair and straight onto the table. ''Now push your golden plate near me,'' said the frog, ''so that we may eat together.'' As she did so, the frog leapt onto her plate and gobbled up all her dinner, which was just as well, because the Princess didn't feel much like eating.

Next, the frog drank from her little golden cup until it was quite empty. Somehow the Princess didn't feel at all thirsty either! After the frog had finished, he took one great leap and landed on the Princess's knee. ''Go away you ugly cold frog!'' she screamed. ''I will never let you sleep on my lovely clean bed!''

This made the King very angry. ''This frog helped you when you needed it. Now you must keep your promise to him.''

"I am very tired after that wonderful meal," the frog said, "and you did promise that I could go to sleep on your golden bed."

Very unwillingly the Princess picked up the frog and carried him upstairs to her room.

When the frog hopped into the middle of her golden bed, it was just too much for the Princess. She tugged hard at the coverlet and tipped the poor frog onto the floor.